THE Ⓧ FILES™

1997 desk diary

THE ⓧ FILES™

1997 desk diary

Voyager
An Imprint of HarperCollins*Publishers*
77-85 Fulham Palace Road,
Hammersmith, London W6 8JB

Published by *Voyager* 1996
1 2 3 4 5 6 7 8 9

We wish to acknowledge the following still photographers for their
photographic contribution to this book:

Michael Grecco
Chris Helcermanas-Benge
Jack Rowand
Ken Staniforth
Marcel Williams

A catalogue record for this book
is available from the British Library

ISBN 0 00 255818 1

Printed and bound in Great Britain by
Scotprint Ltd., Musselburgh

Designed by Derek Walls
Research Assistance Sarah Stegall

Voyager

THE Ⓧ FILES™

1997 desk diary

HarperCollins*Publishers*

1996

january
s	m	t	w	t	f	s
	1	2	3	4	5	6
7	8	9	10	11	12	13
14	15	16	17	18	19	20
21	22	23	24	25	26	27
28	29	30	31			

february
s	m	t	w	t	f	s
				1	2	3
4	5	6	7	8	9	10
11	12	13	14	15	16	17
18	19	20	21	22	23	24
25	26	27	28	29		

march
s	m	t	w	t	f	s
					1	2
3	4	5	6	7	8	9
10	11	12	13	14	15	16
17	18	19	20	21	22	23
24/31	25	26	27	28	29	30

april
s	m	t	w	t	f	s
	1	2	3	4	5	6
7	8	9	10	11	12	13
14	15	16	17	18	19	20
21	22	23	24	25	26	27
28	29	30				

may
s	m	t	w	t	f	s
			1	2	3	4
5	6	7	8	9	10	11
12	13	14	15	16	17	18
19	20	21	22	23	24	25
26	27	28	29	30	31	

june
s	m	t	w	t	f	s
						1
2	3	4	5	6	7	8
9	10	11	12	13	14	15
16	17	18	19	20	21	22
23/30	24	25	26	27	28	29

july
s	m	t	w	t	f	s
	1	2	3	4	5	6
7	8	9	10	11	12	13
14	15	16	17	18	19	20
21	22	23	24	25	26	27
28	29	30	31			

august
s	m	t	w	t	f	s
				1	2	3
4	5	6	7	8	9	10
11	12	13	14	15	16	17
18	19	20	21	22	23	24
25	26	27	28	29	30	31

september
s	m	t	w	t	f	s
1	2	3	4	5	6	7
8	9	10	11	12	13	14
15	16	17	18	19	20	21
22	23	24	25	26	27	28
29	30					

october
s	m	t	w	t	f	s
		1	2	3	4	5
6	7	8	9	10	11	12
13	14	15	16	17	18	19
20	21	22	23	24	25	26
27	28	29	30	31		

november
s	m	t	w	t	f	s
					1	2
3	4	5	6	7	8	9
10	11	12	13	14	15	16
17	18	19	20	21	22	23
24	25	26	27	28	29	30

december
s	m	t	w	t	f	s
1	2	3	4	5	6	7
8	9	10	11	12	13	14
15	16	17	18	19	20	21
22	23	24	25	26	27	28
29	30	31				

1998

january
s	m	t	w	t	f	s
				1	2	3
4	5	6	7	8	9	10
11	12	13	14	15	16	17
18	19	20	21	22	23	24
25	26	27	28	29	30	31

february
s	m	t	w	t	f	s
1	2	3	4	5	6	7
8	9	10	11	12	13	14
15	16	17	18	19	20	21
22	23	24	25	26	27	28

march
s	m	t	w	t	f	s
1	2	3	4	5	6	7
8	9	10	11	12	13	14
15	16	17	18	19	20	21
22	23	24	25	26	27	28
29	30	31				

april
s	m	t	w	t	f	s
			1	2	3	4
5	6	7	8	9	10	11
12	13	14	15	16	17	18
19	20	21	22	23	24	25
26	27	28	29	30		

may
s	m	t	w	t	f	s
					1	2
3	4	5	6	7	8	9
10	11	12	13	14	15	16
17	18	19	20	21	22	23
24/31	25	26	27	28	29	30

june
s	m	t	w	t	f	s
	1	2	3	4	5	6
7	8	9	10	11	12	13
14	15	16	17	18	19	20
21	22	23	24	25	26	27
28	29	30				

july
s	m	t	w	t	f	s
			1	2	3	4
5	6	7	8	9	10	11
12	13	14	15	16	17	18
19	20	21	22	23	24	25
26	27	28	29	30	31	

august
s	m	t	w	t	f	s
						1
2	3	4	5	6	7	8
9	10	11	12	13	14	15
16	17	18	19	20	21	22
23/30	24/31	25	26	27	28	29

september
s	m	t	w	t	f	s
		1	2	3	4	5
6	7	8	9	10	11	12
13	14	15	16	17	18	19
20	21	22	23	24	25	26
27	28	29	30			

october
s	m	t	w	t	f	s
				1	2	3
4	5	6	7	8	9	10
11	12	13	14	15	16	17
18	19	20	21	22	23	24
25	26	27	28	29	30	31

november
s	m	t	w	t	f	s
1	2	3	4	5	6	7
8	9	10	11	12	13	14
15	16	17	18	19	20	21
22	23	24	25	26	27	28
29	30					

december
s	m	t	w	t	f	s
		1	2	3	4	5
6	7	8	9	10	11	12
13	14	15	16	17	18	19
20	21	22	23	24	25	26
27	28	29	30	31		

1997

january
s	m	t	w	t	f	s
			1	2	3	4
5	6	7	8	9	10	11
12	13	14	15	16	17	18
19	20	21	22	23	24	25
26	27	28	29	30	31	

february
s	m	t	w	t	f	s
						1
2	3	4	5	6	7	8
9	10	11	12	13	14	15
16	17	18	19	20	21	22
23	24	25	26	27	28	

march
s	m	t	w	t	f	s
						1
2	3	4	5	6	7	8
9	10	11	12	13	14	15
16	17	18	19	20	21	22
23/30	24/31	25	26	27	28	29

april
s	m	t	w	t	f	s
		1	2	3	4	5
6	7	8	9	10	11	12
13	14	15	16	17	18	19
20	21	22	23	24	25	26
27	28	29	30			

may
s	m	t	w	t	f	s
				1	2	3
4	5	6	7	8	9	10
11	12	13	14	15	16	17
18	19	20	21	22	23	24
25	26	27	28	29	30	31

june
s	m	t	w	t	f	s
1	2	3	4	5	6	7
8	9	10	11	12	13	14
15	16	17	18	19	20	21
22	23	24	25	26	27	28
29	30					

july
s	m	t	w	t	f	s
		1	2	3	4	5
6	7	8	9	10	11	12
13	14	15	16	17	18	19
20	21	22	23	24	25	26
27	28	29	30	31		

august
s	m	t	w	t	f	s
					1	2
3	4	5	6	7	8	9
10	11	12	13	14	15	16
17	18	19	20	21	22	23
24/31	25	26	27	28	29	30

september
s	m	t	w	t	f	s
	1	2	3	4	5	6
7	8	9	10	11	12	13
14	15	16	17	18	19	20
21	22	23	24	25	26	27
28	29	30				

october
s	m	t	w	t	f	s
			1	2	3	4
5	6	7	8	9	10	11
12	13	14	15	16	17	18
19	20	21	22	23	24	25
26	27	28	29	30	31	

november
s	m	t	w	t	f	s
						1
2	3	4	5	6	7	8
9	10	11	12	13	14	15
16	17	18	19	20	21	22
23/30	24	25	26	27	28	29

december
s	m	t	w	t	f	s
	1	2	3	4	5	6
7	8	9	10	11	12	13
14	15	16	17	18	19	20
21	22	23	24	25	26	27
28	29	30	31			

THE TRUTH IS OUT THERE™

HOLIDAYS

january 1, wednesday	new year's day
march 17, monday	st patrick's day (northern ireland & republic of ireland)
march 28, friday	good friday
march 31, monday	easter monday
may 5, monday	may day
may 26, monday	spring bank holiday (u.k.)
june 2, monday	june holiday (republic of ireland)
july 14, monday	orangeman's day holiday (northern ireland)
august 4, monday	august holiday (republic of ireland)
august 25, monday	summer bank holiday (u.k.)
october 27, monday	october holiday (republic of ireland)
december 25, thursday	christmas day
december 26, friday	boxing day

The airplane passenger manifest that Scully
scrutinizes in "Little Green Men" while
trying to trace Mulder's movements, contains
the names of many online X-Files fans.

LITTLE GREEN MEN
First aired: September 16, 1994

DECEMBER/JANUARY

30 monday _____ 31 tuesday _____

_____ _____

_____ _____

_____ _____

_____ _____

_____ _____

1 wednesday (new year's day) _____ 2 thursday _____

_____ _____

_____ _____

_____ _____

_____ _____

_____ _____

3 friday

4 saturday

5 sunday

X

In January 1994, <u>The X-Files</u> won the Golden Globe Award for Best Dramatic Series.

JANUARY

6 monday

7 tuesday

8 wednesday

9 thursday

10 friday

11 saturday

12 sunday

X

January 7, 1948. Captain Thomas Mantell of the U.S. Air Force pursued a UFO he described as "metallic and tremendous in size;" his body and crashed plane were later found after he lost contact with ground control.

JANUARY

13 monday

14 tuesday

15 wednesday

16 thursday

17 friday

18 saturday

19 sunday

X

A rare alignment of the planets, which occurs on January 12, 1996, plunges Mulder and Scully into a town swept up by strange behavior and murderous teens. "SYZYGY"

THE TRUTH IS

JANUARY

20 monday (martin luther king, jr. birthday celebration)

21 tuesday

22 wednesday

23 thursday

24 friday

25 saturday

26 sunday

X

Mulder and Scully investigate
the case of a gender-switching
killer who murders his victims
through sex. "GENDERBENDER"

27 monday

28 tuesday

29 wednesday

30 thursday

31 friday

_____
_____
_____
_____
_____

1 saturday

_____
_____
_____
_____
_____

2 sunday

_____
_____
_____
_____
_____

X
___

In a New Hampshire woods a young boy summoning a demon to impress his date calls up more than he can handle.
"DIE HAND DIE VERLETZT"

The aristocratic British lord, Sir Malcolm Marsden, who is threatened by a pyrokinetic assassin in "Fire," was actually named after the show's chief hairdresser.

FIRE
First aired: December 17, 1993

FEBRUARY

<u>3 monday</u>

<u>4 tuesday</u>

<u>5 wednesday</u>

<u>6 thursday</u>

7 friday

8 saturday

9 sunday

X
___

February 3, 1995. Agent Mulder
arrives in the Arctic Circle
searching for the alien assassin
who killed a clone claiming to
be his sister.
"END GAME"

FEBRUARY

10 monday

11 tuesday

12 wednesday (lincoln's birthday)
(ash wednesday)

13 thursday

14 friday (valentine's day)

_____

_____

_____

_____

_____

_____

15 saturday

_____

_____

_____

_____

_____

16 sunday

_____

_____

_____

_____

_____

X

Mulder's old nemesis, John
Barnett, kills a jewelry store
clerk just to send Mulder a
message—that he's not dead.
"YOUNG AT HEART"

FEBRUARY

17 monday (presidents' day)

_____

_____

_____

_____

_____

18 tuesday

_____

_____

_____

_____

_____

19 wednesday

_____

_____

_____

_____

_____

20 thursday

_____

_____

_____

_____

_____

21 friday

_____
_____
_____
_____
_____
_____

22 saturday (washington's birthday)

_____
_____
_____
_____
_____
_____

23 sunday

_____
_____
_____
_____
_____
_____

X
―――

An Iraqi fighter pilot shoots
down a UFO, and Deep Throat leads
Mulder on a merry chase across
the country looking for it.
"E.B.E."

FEBRUARY/MARCH

24 monday _____

25 tuesday _____

26 wednesday _____

27 thursday _____

28 friday

1 saturday

2 sunday

X

Dana Scully was born February 23, 1964.

The final episode of season one, "The Erlenmeyer Flask," marks the departure from the series of Deep Throat (played by Jerry Hardin), the undercover source for Mulder. His dying words, "Trust no one," are substituted in the teaser for the show's usual "The truth is out there."

THE ERLENMEYER FLASK
First aired: May 13, 1994

MARCH

3 monday

4 tuesday

5 wednesday

6 thursday

7 friday

8 saturday

9 sunday

X

March 6, 1992. Dana Scully is
assigned to the X-Files division
and meets Fox Mulder.
THE X-FILES PILOT

MARCH

10 monday

11 tuesday

12 wednesday

13 thursday

14 friday
_____

_____

_____

_____

_____

_____

15 saturday
_____

_____

_____

_____

_____

16 sunday
_____

_____

_____

_____

_____

_____

X

March 9, 1993. Samuel Hartley
rises from a slab at the
morgue to face down a killer
from his own congregation.
"MIRACLE MAN"

MARCH

<u>17 monday</u> (st. patrick's day)   <u>18 tuesday</u>

<u>19 wednesday</u>   <u>20 thursday</u>

21 friday

22 saturday

23 sunday (palm sunday)

X

Mulder and Scully close their first case together on March 22, 1992 by subjecting Billy Miles to hypnotic regression; Miles claims to have been abducted and to have had implants inserted in his sinuses.

THE X-FILES PILOT

MARCH

<u>24 monday</u>

<u>25 tuesday</u>

<u>26 wednesday</u>

<u>27 thursday</u>

28 friday (good friday)

29 saturday

30 sunday (easter)

X

March 27, 1994. Mulder and
Scully open the file on
Michelle Bishop, a little girl
who may house the soul of a
murdered cop. "BORN AGAIN"

The bones and skulls used in "Aubrey" are not
real bones. They are plastic bones which
must be "aged" with paint and chemicals, and
have the plastic seams filed off. Real bones
would cost a great deal more.

AUBREY
First aired: January 6, 1995

MARCH/APRIL

31 monday (easter monday-canada)

1 tuesday

2 wednesday

3 thursday

4 friday

5 saturday

6 sunday (daylight saving time begins)

X

A bizarre murder in a circus town draws Mulder and Scully into an investigation involving sideshow freaks and geeks. "HUMBUG"

7 monday

8 tuesday

9 wednesday

10 thursday

11 friday

12 saturday

13 sunday

X

April 9, 1995. An earthquake
on a Navajo reservation in
Arizona uncovers a buried box-
car full of what appear to be
alien bodies.
"ANASAZI"

APRIL

14 monday

15 tuesday

16 wednesday

17 thursday

18 friday

19 saturday

20 sunday

X

April 16, 1995. "The Thinker"
is found murdered in a Trenton
dump site, alerting Scully to
Fox Mulder's frame-up for his
father's murder. "BLESSING WAY"

APRIL

21 monday

22 tuesday (passover begins)

Meeting in DC at 2:00pm
RAF meeting also. at 1:40pm

23 wednesday

Lecture on South Africa in
Assembly Hall Lessons 5 &6

24 thursday

25 friday

26 saturday

RAF competition, dep 11:30

27 sunday

RAF competition

X

April 25, 1994. Mentally
retarded janitor Roland Fuller,
under the psychic control of
his dead twin, kills a scien-
tist by holding his head in a
vat of liquid nitrogen.
"ROLAND"

28 monday

29 tuesday

Mock Trial - Dutton Centre,
in Lessons 2 and 3

Heights and Weights.

30 wednesday

Lesson 5 &6 - Lecture on
Gap Year

General Studies meal

1 thursday

School general Elections

2 friday

3 saturday

4 sunday

X

May 2, 1993. Lula Phillips,
released from prison, begins a
crime spree with Warren Dupre.
"LAZARUS"

The Flukeman costume in "The Host" was a true ordeal for actor Darin Morgan. Originally it took six hours to put on before technicians were able to speed up the process, and at one point in the filming Morgan had to wear the costume for 20 consecutive hours.

THE HOST
First aired: September 23, 1994

MAY

5 monday

3:10 pm Saturday Period 1
3:50 pm Saturday Period 2

6 tuesday

7 wednesday

Lecture: Health Issues, in
D.C., lessons 5 & 6.

8 thursday

9 friday

4:30 pm   Exeat begins

10 saturday

Driving Theory Test

11 sunday (mother's day)

Return to School for 9:00 pm

X

May 8, 1994. Dr. Secare, a man
cured of cancer by alien gene
therapy, is shot by Baltimore
police and bleeds green blood.
"THE ERLENMEYER FLASK"

12 monday

13 tuesday

Visit to Liverpool Uni

14 wednesday

Lecture: Health Issues, in the
D.C., lessons 5 + 6

15 thursday

York Uni

16 friday

17 saturday

18 sunday

X

George Kearns meets a grisly
end at the hands of cannibals
in the small town of Dudley,
Arkansas. "OUR TOWN"

MAY

19 monday (victoria day-canada)

3.10pm Saturday Period 3
3.50pm Saturday Period 4

20 tuesday

21 wednesday

Newcastle Uni + Umist

22 thursday

23 friday

24 saturday

4:30pm   Half Term begins

25 sunday

X

Under the influence of a drug
planted in his tap water,
Mulder hits Skinner in the
face. "ANASAZI"

26 **monday** (memorial day)

27 **tuesday**

28 **wednesday**

29 **thursday**

30 friday

31 saturday

1 sunday

9.00 pm Return to School

X

May 26, 1994. Assistant
Director Walter Skinner, acting
on orders, closes the X-Files
and re-assigns Mulder and
Scully to other duties.
"THE ERLENMEYER FLASK"

Mulder tells Roland a dream he (Mulder) had, wherein he dove down into a pool searching for his father. In the script, Mulder was searching for his sister.

ROLAND
First aired: May 6, 1994

JUNE

2 monday

3 tuesday

4 wednesday

5 thursday

6 friday

7 saturday

8 sunday

X

June 3, 1985. Duane Barry is abducted from his home in Pulaski, Virginia. "DUANE BARRY"

JUNE

9 monday

10 tuesday

11 wednesday

12 thursday

13 friday

14 saturday (flag day)

15 sunday (father's day)

The football game that Mulder and Scully miss in order to investigate a grisly serial killer is Washington v. Minnesota, two teams that each had a "Carter" in their ranks. In one scene a television announcer mentions a catch by Cris Carter. "IRRESISTIBLE"

JUNE

16 monday

17 tuesday

18 wednesday

19 thursday

20 friday

21 saturday

22 sunday

June 16, 1989. Fox Mulder
undergoes hypnotic regression
with Dr. Heitz Verber and
recovers memories of his sister's abduction. "CONDUIT"

JUNE

23 monday

24 tuesday (st. jean-baptiste day-
canada)

25 wednesday

26 thursday

27 friday

28 saturday

29 sunday

X

June 24, 1947. Kenneth Arnold's historic sighting of disks flying over the Cascade Mountains gave rise to the phrase "flying saucers," the first use of the term in UFO literature.

The concept for "Dod Kalm" was built around
access the X-Files crew had to a Canadian
navy destroyer. The writers were specifically
asked to tailor a script around that setting.

DOD KALM
First aired: March 10, 1995

JUNE/JULY

<u>30 monday</u>

<u>1 tuesday</u>   (canada day—canada)

<u>2 wednesday</u>

<u>3 thursday</u>

4 friday   (independence day)

5 saturday

6 sunday

X

July 2, 1947 Witnesses claimed to
have found a crashed UFO on a
ranch outside Roswell, NM.
Although government reports
initially labeled it a "flying
disk," later reports claimed that
it was a weather balloon.

JULY

7 monday _____

_____

_____

_____

_____

8 tuesday _____

_____

_____

_____

_____

9 wednesday _____

_____

_____

_____

_____

10 thursday _____

_____

_____

_____

_____

11 friday

12 saturday

13 sunday

X

July 7, 1994. Mulder flies to Puerto Rico to investigate the possibility of extraterrestrial contact. "LITTLE GREEN MEN"

JULY

14 monday

15 tuesday

16 wednesday

17 thursday

18 friday

19 saturday

20 sunday

![X]

Chris Carter has appeared on
The X-Files only once: he was
one of the FBI panel members
interviewing Scully in the
episode "ANASAZI."

JULY

21 monday _____

22 tuesday _____

_____

_____

_____

_____

_____

_____

23 wednesday _____

24 thursday _____

_____

_____

_____

_____

_____

_____

25 friday

26 saturday

27 sunday

X

July 23, 1993. Eugene Victor
Tooms is arrested for tearing
the liver out of George
Usher, but is released after
he passes a lie detector test.
"SQUEEZE"

JULY/AUGUST

28 monday

29 tuesday

30 wednesday

31 thursday

1 friday

2 saturday

3 sunday

X

Senator Richard Matheson, who
sends Mulder to Arecibo,
Puerto Rico, is named for
science fiction and horror
writer Richard "Somewhere in
Time" Matheson.

Nisei: Second-generation Japanese-Americans.
In the episode by that title the term refers
to the subjects of experiments conducted by a
Japanese war criminal in the United States.

NISEI
First aired: January 6, 1995

AUGUST

4 monday

5 tuesday

6 wednesday

7 thursday

8 friday

_____

_____

_____

_____

_____

_____

9 saturday

_____

_____

_____

_____

_____

10 sunday

_____

_____

_____

_____

_____

_____

X
—

David Duchovny born August 7,
1960.

Gillian Anderson born August 9,
1968.

AUGUST

11 monday

12 tuesday

13 wednesday

14 thursday

15 friday

16 saturday

17 sunday

X

August 10, 1944. On a bomber
mission over India, Capt. A. M.
Reida sighted "foo fighters"
following his craft. He
described spheres "five or six
feet in diameter, bright orange"
which paced his plane at
210 mph.

AUGUST

18 monday

19 tuesday

20 wednesday

21 thursday

22 friday

23 saturday

24 sunday

X

August 19, 1953. A sailor
dying of radiation burns tells
Bill Mulder and the young
Cigarette-Smoking Man of his
submarine's suicide mission to
guard a sunken UFO. "APOCRYPHA"

AUGUST

25 monday

26 tuesday

27 wednesday

28 thursday

29 friday

30 saturday

31 sunday

X

August 29, 1995. Dana Scully
attempts to autopsy the remains
of Lauren MacKalvey and finds
most of the fatty tissue miss-
ing from her corpse. "2 SHY"

The case of Phineas Gage, which Scully refers
to in "Duane Barry," actually happened.
In the early part of this century, a railway worker
placing dynamite set off an explosion that drove a
three-foot-long steel rod through his brain. Gage
not only survived but suffered no physical
impairment and went on to live another 20
years. However, his personality underwent a
dramatic change, turning him into an irascible,
profane, and thoroughly unpleasant man.

DUANE BARRY
First aired: October 14, 1994

SEPTEMBER

1 monday (labor day)

2 tuesday

3 wednesday

4 thursday

5 friday

6 saturday

7 sunday

X

"Crowley" High School evokes
the memory of British ceremoni-
alist Aleister Crowley, whose
theories on "magick" shocked
his contemporaries and heavily
influenced the development of
modern Wicca.
"DIE HAND DIE VERLETZT"

SEPTEMBER

8 monday

9 tuesday

10 wednesday

11 thursday

12 friday _____

_____

_____

_____

_____

_____

13 saturday _____

_____

_____

_____

_____

14 sunday _____

_____

_____

_____

_____

_____

X

September 12, 1995. Darren
Peter Oswald sets a new record
on a video game after killing
a pizza delivery boy with a
lightning bolt. "D.P.O."

SEPTEMBER

15 monday

16 tuesday

17 wednesday

18 thursday

19 friday

20 saturday

21 sunday

X

September 16, 1995. Clyde
Bruckman finds the body of a
murdered fortune-teller; Mulder
discovers Bruckman is psychic.
"CLYDE BRUCKMAN'S FINAL REPOSE"

SEPTEMBER

22 monday

23 tuesday

24 wednesday

25 thursday

26 friday

27 saturday

28 sunday

X

Piper Maru Anderson, Gillian
Anderson's daughter, born
September 25, 1994.

Deep Throat's warning in the "Fallen Angel" episode is a quote from Don Corleone in The Godfather. "Keep your friends close, but keep your enemies closer."

FALLEN ANGEL
First aired: November 19, 1993

SEPTEMBER/OCTOBER

29 monday

30 tuesday

1 wednesday

2 thursday (rosh hashanah)

3 friday

4 saturday

5 sunday

X

October 1, 1993. Mulder and Scully investigate the abduction of a young girl, prompting Mulder to confront his feelings about his own sister's disappearance. "CONDUIT"

OCTOBER

6 monday

7 tuesday

8 wednesday

9 thursday

10 friday

11 saturday (yom kippur)

12 sunday

X

October 5, 1993. Howard
Graves is murdered and his
death made to look like suicide; his ghost returns to
protect his secretary.
"SHADOWS"

OCTOBER

13 monday (columbus day) (thanksgiving-canada)

14 tuesday

15 wednesday

16 thursday

17 friday

18 saturday

19 sunday

X

Fox Mulder born October 13, 1961.
Series creator Chris Carter
born October 13, 1956. "Ten
Thirteen Productions" is named
for his birthday.

OCTOBER

20 monday

21 tuesday

22 wednesday

23 thursday

24 friday

25 saturday

26 sunday (daylight
saving time ends)

X

October 24, 1993. Mulder and
Scully investigate the locked-
room murder of a man; suspicion
falls on a self-aware computer
of murderous intent.
"GHOST IN THE MACHINE"

27 monday

28 tuesday

29 wednesday

30 thursday

31 friday (halloween)

1 saturday

2 sunday

X

October 27, 1995. Virgil Incanto's skin, found at the scene of one of his crimes, reveals his unusual disorder and sends Mulder and Scully looking for a "fat-sucking vampire." "2 SHY"

The design which appears on a tree in the beginning of "Fresh Bones" is a "vever," a sign belonging to the spirits honored in voudoun. As Bauvais explains, the vever is a loco-miroir, or mirror of the soul.

FRESH BONES
First aired: February 3, 1995

NOVEMBER

3 monday

4 tuesday (election day)

5 wednesday

6 thursday

<u>7 friday</u>

<u>8 saturday</u>

<u>9 sunday</u>

X

November 5, 1993. Mulder and
Scully investigate the deaths
of an entire Arctic research
crew and find themselves
trapped with an alien parasite.
"ICE"

NOVEMBER

10 monday

11 tuesday

12 wednesday

13 thursday

14 friday

_____

_____

_____

_____

_____

_____

15 saturday

_____

_____

_____

_____

_____

16 sunday

_____

_____

_____

_____

_____

_____

X

November 14, 1994. Donnie
Pfaster, arrested for assault-
ing a girl in his classroom,
catches sight of Agent Scully
and targets her for his next
victim. "IRRESISTIBLE"

NOVEMBER

17 monday

18 tuesday

19 wednesday

20 thursday

21 friday _____

22 saturday _____

23 sunday _____

X

Samantha Mulder born November 21,
1965. "PAPER CLIP."

NOVEMBER

24 monday

25 tuesday

26 wednesday

27 thursday (thanksgiving day-u.s.)

28 friday

29 saturday

30 sunday

X

November 27, 1973. Agent Fox
Mulder's sister Samantha is
abducted from their home.
Mulder later remembers "a
presence in the room" and a
bright light, and believes she
was taken by aliens.
"LITTLE GREEN MEN"

"**O**ne Breath" was filmed just days after Gillian Anderson gave birth to her daughter Piper by cesarean section. Scully spends most of the episode lying in a hospital bed, unconscious, while Mulder fights to save her life.

ONE BREATH
First aired: November 11, 1994

DECEMBER

1 monday

2 tuesday

3 wednesday

4 thursday

5 friday

6 saturday

7 sunday

X

"3" is the only episode to be
made without Gillian Anderson.

DECEMBER

8 monday

_____

_____

_____

_____

_____

_____

9 tuesday

_____

_____

_____

_____

_____

_____

10 wednesday

_____

_____

_____

_____

_____

11 thursday

_____

_____

_____

_____

_____

12 friday

13 saturday

14 sunday

X

December 11, 1984. Los Angeles
TV producer Jaime Shandera
received the famous "Majestic
12" documents, purportedly
proving that the government
covered up the existence of
a UFO recovered from the
Roswell crash.

DECEMBER

15 monday

16 tuesday

17 wednesday

18 thursday

19 friday

_____
_____
_____
_____
_____
_____

20 saturday

_____
_____
_____
_____
_____

21 sunday

_____
_____
_____
_____
_____
_____

X

Scully and Mulder clash over
the causes of a stigmata in
young Kevin Cryder, even as a
diabolical killer stalks
the boy. "REVELATIONS"

DECEMBER

22 monday _____

23 tuesday _____

24 wednesday (hanukkah begins) _____

25 thursday (christmas) _____

<u>26 friday</u> (boxing day) canada

<u>27 saturday</u>

<u>28 sunday</u>

X

Captain William Scully, Agent
Dana Scully's father, dies
between Christmas 1993 and New
Year's 1994. "BEYOND THE SEA"

29 monday

30 tuesday

31 wednesday

1 thursday (new year's day)

2 friday _____

3 saturday _____

4 sunday _____

X

December 29, 1994. "Dr.
Landon Prince," one of the
cloned Gregors, is killed by
an alien assassin sent to wipe
out the group's attempt to
hybridize humans and aliens.
"COLONY"

NOTES

NOTES

THE TRUTH IS OUT THERE™